IMAGINE THAT

Licensed exclusively to Imagine That Publishing Ltd
Tide Mill Way, Woodbridge, Suffolk, IP12 1AP, UK
www.imaginethat.com
Copyright © 2019 Imagine That Group Ltd
All rights reserved
2 4 6 8 9 7 5 3 1
Manufactured in China

Written by Isadora Rose
Illustrated by Gavin Scott

ISBN 978-1-78958-300-7

A catalogue record for this book is available from the British Library

Happiness is...

Isadora Rose

Gavin Scott

Happiness is holding hands with a friend.

Looking for the rainbow's end.

Jumping in a muddy puddle.

Warming up with a cuddle.

Laughing at a funny joke.

Fixing something old that broke.

A playful puppy or a kitten.

A newborn baby wearing mittens.

Story time with mum and dad.

Cheering up someone who's sad.

Visiting somewhere new.

Stopping to admire the view.

Dancing to the music's beat.

Waving arms and tapping feet.

Swimming where sea meets the land.

Running, playing on the sand.

Smiling as you say, 'Hello'.

Rolling in fresh, fallen snow.

Playing on the swings and slide.

Taking your bike for a ride.

Happiness is ...

Love.